CATHERINE E. PUGH

Illustrations by Andre Forde

C. E. Pugh
Baltimore

This Book Belongs To:

_____

_____

_____

_____

Hi, I'm Healthy Holly and I want to be your friend. I want you to exercise and eat right like me. Exercise is moving your body. My parents and my doctor say that if we exercise and eat right we will live a long time and have fun like them. They say the things we do growing up will follow us when we become big people. That means we will exercise when we get older too. When we exercise and eat right we cut down on our chances of getting sick. Nobody wants to be sick and I don't want you to be sick. I want you to be healthy like me.

Exercise needs to become a part of our daily lives. Everyone should spend some part of their day moving. Exercise happens when we walk, run, dance, jump rope, ride bikes, swim, play tennis, baseball, basketball and almost any sport.

The fun part about exercise is that you can do it by yourself or with family and friends. I hope you enjoy my first book and want to read the others. Welcome to my world where exercising is fun!!!

Healthy Holly

Holly is a happy girl.
Holly and her mother have just come from a **walk**.
They like taking long **walks**.

1

They **walk** to the library.

They **walk** around the lake.

They take **walks** to her grandparents' house.

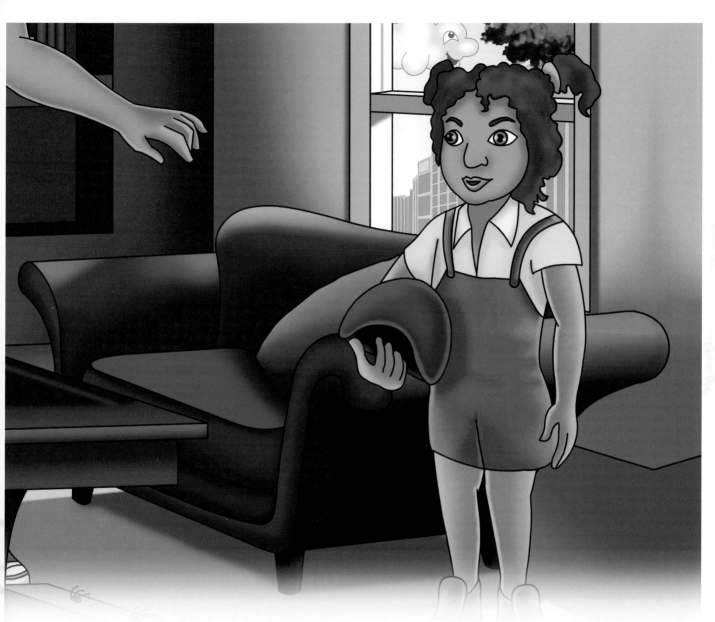

It is Saturday morning. "Holly get your helmet. Your father and I are going to the park on our bikes. We need to get some exercise. **Exercise** keeps us **healthy**," said her mother.

Holly's mother and father would take turns. They would **ride** Holly on the back of their bikes. When they came home, Holly asked, "What is **exercise**? Can it make me **healthy**?"

Holly and her parents **danced** around the room.
Exercise is doing good things with your body.

"**Exercise** is when we **walk** and **ride** our bikes. It is when we play **tennis**. It is when we **swim**," said Holly's father.

"I like going to the park with you and dad." said Holly.
I want to **ride** my own bike. You said it makes you
healthy. May I have a bike for my next birthday? Asked Holly.

"Maybe Holly is old enough to have a bike," said her father.
Holly's mother and father went to the bike store.

They bought Holly a bike. "We will give it to her on her birthday," said her parents. When it was Holly's birthday they hid the bike in the yard.

"Surprise!" said her parents as they **walked** to the yard.
"I have my own bike. Will you show me how to **ride** it?"
smiled Holly.

Holly's mother and father took turns teaching her to **ride** her bike. Soon Holly was able to **ride** her bike. On Saturdays, Holly **rode** her bike with her parents to the park. Holly likes to **exercise**.

"**Exercising** is fun," said Holly's mother. "I will be healthy,"
says Holly. "I like having fun."
The next day, Holly's mother gave her a surprise.

14

"What is in the box?" asked Holly. It is a gift to help you stay **healthy**," said her mother. Holly sat down and opened the box and pulled out a long rope. "What do I do with this?" she asked.

Holly's mother took her outside, took the rope and said,
"Let me show you." Holly's mother began to **jump rope**.
She gave the rope to Holly. It was Holly's turn to jump rope.

Holly kept trying to do it. She was laughing while trying to **jump**. Holly was having fun. "Oh, look at you. Holly you are **jumping rope**. You are **exercising**," said her mother.

"I like **jumping rope**," said Holly. I can do it whenever I want.

She **jumps rope** by herself. She **jumps rope** with her mother. Holly **jumps rope** with her friends.

Holly gets lots of **exercise**. She has fun **jumping rope**. She has fun **riding** her bike. Holly has fun **walking** to her grandparents' house. "Just call me Healthy Holly," she says with a smile.

A Parent's Guide To Helping Your Child Exercise

According to the National Institute of Health, children should be doing a certain amount of exercise according to their age. Parents should limit TV, video games and computer time. Like my parents, they should set a good example by being physically active themselves. Exercising together can be fun for everyone. Below I have provided you with a chart that identifies the kind of activity you should be doing according to your age.

2 to 3 Year Old
30 minutes of structured physical activity (adult led). Get at least 60 minutes un-structured physical activity (free play). Limit inactivity to no longer than 1 hour at a time except when sleeping.

Skills 2 to 3 Year Old
By age 2 should be able to walk, run, jump in place, with both feet. By age 3 run and jump well. Balance on one foot, climb well, kick the ball forward; throw the ball overhand, and pedal a tricycle.

4 to 5 year old
60 minutes of structured physical activity (adult led activity). Get at least 60 minutes unstructured physical activity (free play). Limit inactivity to no longer than 1 hour at a time unless sleeping.

Skills 4 to 5 Year Old
By age 4 you should be learning to hop, skip, jump forward, catch a ball, balance on one foot (for 5 seconds or longer) or do a somersault. Pre-schoolers may also enjoy dancing, swimming, hiking, or tricycle and bicycle.

6 to 12 year old
Get 60 minutes or more of moderate and vigorous physical activity. Limit inactivity to no longer than 2 hours. Avoid periods of inactivity of two hours or more.

Skills 6 to 12 Year Old
Begin to engage in organized sports. Incorporate into daily routine after dinner walks. More free play, including playing tag, and riding bikes.

My Favorite Exercises Are:

_____

_____

_____

_____

_____

_____

_____

_____